Creation and Evolution

Studies in
Christianity
and
Science

Colin Humphreys

Contents

Oxford University Press 1985

Oxford University Press, Walton Street, Oxford OX2 6DP

Oxford
New York Toronto Melbourne Auckland
Petaling Jaya Singapore Hong Kong Tokyo
Delhi Bombay Calcutta Madras Karachi
Nairobi Dar es Salaam Cape Town

and associated companies in
Beirut Berlin Ibadan Nicosia

Oxford is a trade mark of Oxford University Press

© C J Humphreys 1985

ISBN 0 19 832130 9

These booklets are produced by an ecumenical group of scientists, philosophers and theologians, supported by an advisory panel of experts in each particular field

The purpose of this series is to allow practising Christians, who are experts in a particular field of science or social studies, to express a personal view of problems related to that field. The opinions of each author are his or her own and are not necessarily those of the series editor, nor the Advisory Committee.

Typeset by Set Fair

Printed in Hong Kong

The cover painting is Michaelangelo's Creation of Adam, by permission of the Bridgeman Art Library/Vatican.

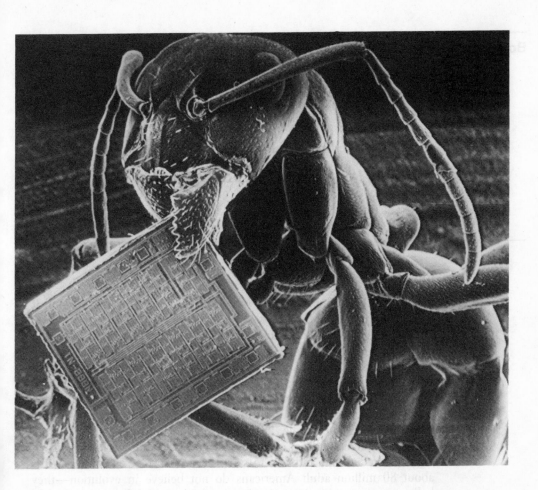

Creation and Evolution Electron micrograph of a silicon chip being gripped in the jaws of an ant. The actual size of the silicon chip is 2mm x 2mm. The chip is very complex, and contains 2600 transistors. (By comparison a transistor radio contains up to 30 transistors.) It has been designed by man but the design has evolved over 30 years.

Now look at the ant. It is also very complex, in fact far more complex than the silicon chip. It can see, breathe, move, reproduce and sleep, and carry loads twice its own weight. Was it created by God in this form? Or has it evolved from something else over the years?

(*Micrograph recorded on a Philips scanning electron microscope.*)

1   Creation versus Evolution

Box 1   **Is there a conflict?**

Evolution—The Fossils Say No!
(Title of Book by Duane Gish, 1973)

Evolution is proven.
(Mark Ridley, in *Darwin Up-to-date*, 1983)

Darwinism removed the whole idea of God as the creator of organisms.
(Sir Julian Huxley, in TV programme, 1959)

Half of all adult Americans believe God created Adam and Eve to start the human race.
(American Gallup Poll, 1979)

1.1   Introduction

Sacking a schoolteacher is a very rare event in Britain. It can occur only if the teacher has committed a serious offence or is guilty of gross professional misconduct. In 1977, Hertfordshire County Council dismissed a teacher of religious education, Mr D. C. C. Watson. He had committed the 'offence' of teaching that animals and plants did not develop over millions of years by a process of **evolution**, as described in the school textbooks, but were created directly by God in six days.

These beliefs are called **creationism**, and they are shared by a great many people. For example, in 1979, a Gallup Poll in America showed that approximately half of all Americans aged 18 and over believed that 'God created Adam and Eve to start the human race.' In other words about 80 million adult Americans do not believe in evolution—they believe in creationism instead. The current American President, Ronald Reagan, supports the creationists' campaign to give equal time in biology lessons to evolution and creationism. Some American biology books for schools already give equal treatment to both beliefs.

In Britain, support for creationism is not nearly as strong as it is in America, but it is undoubtedly gaining ground. There are three main British creationist societies. The largest, the Creation Science Movement (formerly the Evolution Protest Group) has quadrupled its

4

membership in the past 20 years. A quarter of a million copies of its booklet *Evolution: Science Falsely So-called* have been printed. Other British creationist societies are the Newton Scientific Association and the Biblical Creation Society. The latter was founded in 1977 and now has over 700 members, mostly university graduates.

Biology books used in British schools rarely, if ever, mention creationism. Most put forward evolution as an established fact. This book tries to present the key evidence for evolution in an unbiased way. But first you must make sure that you understand the terms evolution, Darwinism, creation and creationism. They are all explained below.

1.2 Evolution

Walk into any zoo and look at the amazing variety of animals. Elephants and emus, penguins and parrots, lions and lizards, monkeys and men. How have all these different animals come into existence? Of particular importance to us, where has man come from?

For many people, evolution provides the answer. The theory of evolution proposes that all animals and plants have developed from one, or a few, original single cells. The original single cell (or cells) is itself presumed to have arisen from non-living matter. There are various theories about *how* evolution may have occurred. The best-known of these is **Darwinism**. In fact, most school textbooks give *only* Darwin's theory of evolution.

1.3 Darwinism

In 1831 Charles Darwin, a twenty-four-year-old Englishman, set off on HMS *Beagle* for a round-the-world voyage that was to cause a revolution in biology. One of the places he visited was the Galapagos Islands, an isolated group of rocky volcanic islands in the Pacific Ocean about 1000 kilometres (600 miles) from the South American mainland. Darwin was astonished by what he found there. For example, there were giant tortoises so big that he could ride on their backs. Some islands had lots of short plants, and on these islands the tortoises had short necks. Other islands were more barren with very few short plants, and on these the tortoises had much longer necks.

Darwin thought he could explain this, and he argued as follows. Imagine a group of tortoises searching for food. The tortoises with short necks can reach only those leaves that are close to the ground. Those with longer necks can reach higher leaves. When all the low leaves are eaten the tortoises with the shorter necks starve to death. The longer-necked tortoises survive and breed, giving birth to similar longer-necked offspring. In each generation, if there is a shortage of food, only those tortoises with the longest necks survive. Thus, after many generations, tortoises on the more barren islands will have longer necks than those on the islands with plenty of short plants. Darwin called this process selection by nature, or *natural selection*.

For over twenty years Darwin pondered on the process. If it could produce longer-necked tortoises, could it also produce a new species? Could it ultimately be the way in which all life evolved? He decided it was, and in 1859 he published his book *The Origin of Species*. This sold out completely on the first day it was published, and has probably had more impact than any other scientific book ever written. In it Darwin put forward the theory that all life has evolved through a process of natural selection, which acts on the slight differences (mutations) that are displayed by every new-born individual.

Darwin used birds as an example. He suggested that, thousands of years ago, birds from the South American mainland had reached the Galapagos Islands. Once there they slowly changed, from generation to generation, to suit their new homes, until eventually they became different species. Darwin himself discovered 13 new species of finches on the Galapagos Islands; these species exist nowhere else in the world. The finches, and the Galapagos tortoises, were probably the strongest evidence Darwin had for his theory of natural selection.

The differences between the Galapagos species of finches and those on the mainland are only small. But if such small changes *had* taken place, asked Darwin, was it not also possible for *major* changes to take place over *millions* of years? He suggested that, very slowly and gradually, by natural selection, fish had developed muscular fins and crawled onto land to become amphibians. Amphibians had then developed water-tight skins and become reptiles, reptiles had developed into mammals, and ultimately man had emerged.

Darwin's theory is in a way so simple it seems almost obvious. The key question is, is it correct? Did new species really form in this way? Have major changes, such as the change from reptiles to mammals, really occurred over millions of years by a process of natural selection?

1.4 Creation

Christians, and people of many other religions, believe that there is a God who created the universe and everything in it. However, many Christians believe that the Bible story of creation is not meant to be a scientific description of the way creation was carried out. These Christians find no difficulty in accepting that God's way of working may have been slow and gradual, and that all of life may have developed from a single cell, over millions and millions of years.

Thus for many Christians there is no conflict between evolution and creation. They believe that evolution is the way in which God chose to create all living things. For them, the question of *how* evolution occurred is a scientific one, to be judged on scientific evidence, and not on religious grounds.

1.5 Creationism

Some Christians believe in creationism. Creationism is sometimes called **special creation** or **creation science**. Creationists believe that the first few chapters of Genesis, the first book of the Bible, should be interpreted as a literal and scientific description of the origin of life.

It follows that creationists believe that one species cannot have evolved from another: all species have been directly created by God. Most creationists believe that creation occurred in literally 6 days.

In 1660, James Ussher, Archbishop of Armagh in Ireland, worked out that Adam was created in 4004 BC. Ussher based his calculations on the Bible, using the age given for Adam when his sons were born, the sons' ages when their sons were born and so on, and adding up all the figures. Some Bibles still have 4004 BC as a footnote at the start of Genesis. Since creationists believe in a literal interpretation of Genesis they therefore believe in a 'young Earth' too. However, some believe that the Bible may have omitted some generations and that the Earth may be up to 10 000 years old, rather than the 6000 years proposed by Ussher. Either way this is enormously different from the 4600 million years claimed by evolutionists.

1.6 Creationism or Darwinism: is either correct?

Despite the enormous number of books on evolution, it is difficult to find

Box 2	Two key questions		
Question	Answers		The Evidence
	Creationism	*Darwinism*	
How old is life on Earth?	About 10 000 years	Many millions of years	See Chapter 2
Does the fossil record show intermediate forms?	No	Yes	See Chapter 3

books which ask and answer the key questions that will help us make up our minds. Two of the most important questions are shown in Box 2.

The first question is 'How old is life on Earth?' Darwin's theory requires it to be very old, many millions of years, since a lot of time is needed for the slow and gradual changes he proposed. On the other hand, creationists believe in a 'young Earth', up to 10 000 years old. We look at evidence for the age of life on Earth more closely in Chapter 2.

The second important question concerns fossils. Fossils are the remains or traces of plants and animals preserved in the earth from ancient times. If Darwinism is correct we would expect lots of 'intermediate' fossils, of species that have since died out. For example, Darwinists postulate that when fishes evolved into amphibians their fins gradually turned into feet. We would therefore expect lots of fossils with half-formed feet. But creationists believe that each species was individually and directly created by God, which means there should be no intermediate fossils. We will look at the facts about fossils in Chapter 3.

Let us end this chapter with an interesting thought. What if the evidence in Chapter 2 shows that the Earth is very old, and the evidence in Chapter 3 shows that few intermediate fossils have been found? Can creationism and Darwinism both be wrong?

Questions

1.1 Explain what is meant by the terms *evolution* and *Darwinism*.

1.2 Darwin used the idea of natural selection to explain the long necks of some tortoises. Think of another example of an animal feature that could possibly be explained using this idea, and then write down your explanation.

1.3 Some people believe in creation and some in creationism. Explain the difference between the two beliefs.

2 How old is life on Earth?

Box 3 | **This is the Age of the Earth**

The world was created on 22 October, 4004 BC at 6 o'clock in the evening.
Archbishop James Ussher, *Chronologia Sacra*, Oxford 1660.

The age of the Earth can be calculated to be about 10 000 years.
Dr A. J. Monty White, *What About Origins?*, 1978.

The age of the Earth is 4600 million years.
Dr John Thackray, Geological Museum Handbook, 1980.

2.1 A walk back through time

One weekend a while ago I travelled back hundreds of millions of years in time, according to the booklet I was carrying. I had been doing research work in Arizona, and took a weekend off to visit the Grand Canyon, one of the seven natural wonders of the world. The Grand Canyon is enormous and magnificent. It is 217 miles long, and an average of 9 miles wide and 1 mile deep. It was formed by the Colorado River slowly cutting its way through layer after layer of rock, like a knife cutting through a many-layered cake. The rocks through which the river cut still lie roughly horizontal, layer upon layer, red, yellow and brown. They are mainly sandstones and limestones, and their colours are especially beautiful in the reddish glow of sunrise and sunset.

It is a tough walk down to the bottom of the Canyon, taking 3 to 5 hours, and an even tougher walk up, taking 5 to 7. Why does it take so long? Well, the rough tracks are steep and winding, and the weather is a problem too. In winter the Canyon is covered with thick snow, and in summer the temperature at the bottom is well over 100°F. In spring and autumn there is snow at the top and great heat at the bottom! In summer it is essential to carry drinking water, at least one gallon per person. And if you are too lazy to walk you can hire a mule. But I digress from the point of my story: geologists agree that as you walk (or ride) down the Canyon the rocks you pass get older and older. The rocks were laid down layer by layer, so it follows that a lower layer must be older than an upper one if the rocks have not been grossly disturbed. Thus, in my walk down the Grand Canyon, I was effectively walking back in time.

How far back? According to my booklet, the rocks at the top of the Canyon are about 200 million years old. That figure was arrived at by a method called radioactive dating. These upper rocks contain some fossils, which are those of reptiles. There are also reptile tracks, and the impressions of insect wings and fern leaves. However, there is *no sign* of mammals or birds. Evolutionists conclude from this evidence that 200 million years ago reptiles, insects and ferns existed, but mammals and birds did not.

Further down the Canyon, about halfway down, there are limestone rocks dated around 400 million years old. These show no signs of reptiles, but they do contain fish fossils. Evolutionists therefore conclude that reptiles did not exist 400 million years ago, while fish did. Still further down, the rocks are thought to be around 500 million years old, and contain some shell fossils and what look like the trails of worms.

But are those dates of rocks and fossils correct? In this chapter we look at two ways scientists use to date the past: counting tree-rings, and radioactive dating. We then look at how creationists explain the fossils in the Grand Canyon and other places. Finally we decide who is right about the age of the earth: creationists with their figure of 10 000 years, or evolutionists with theirs of 4600 million years.

2.2 Counting tree-rings

Many parks contain tree-stumps for people to sit on. By counting the number of bright or dark rings in a stump, one can tell the age of the tree when it was cut down. In spring, a tree grows rapidly, and this produces a new outer ring of light-coloured wood. In summer, the growth is slower and this produces a ring of dark-coloured wood. In winter there is no growth and no ring. Next spring another light-coloured ring is formed, and so on. Hence the age of the tree when it was felled can be found by counting the rings. This method of dating is called **dendrochronology**.

Some trees live for an astonishingly long time. Until 1955, the oldest known trees were sequoia trees, some of which had lived for up to 2000 years. Then even older trees called bristlecone pines were discovered in the White Mountains of California. The oldest known living bristlecone pine is 4900 years old. It is not only the oldest living tree, it is the oldest known living thing, plant or animal, in the world! Fortunately it was not cut down to determine its age. A small horizontal bore-hole was drilled from the outside of the trunk into the centre, the core of wood was extracted, and the rings counted. The tree survived that treatment and is still alive today.

A tree's rings can vary a great deal in colour and thickness from year to year, depending on the local climate. This is a very useful fact. Over a number of years a distinctive pattern of thick and thin rings is built up in the tree, and the same pattern can be picked out in the wood of the other trees in the same region. Using such patterns, scientists can link outer rings of old dead trees with inner rings of young ones, and build up a continuous sequence of tree-rings, going as far back as there is wood available from trees long dead.

By counting tree-rings from both living and dead trees, and examining the patterns in them, a continuous tree-ring dating sequence has been built up, extending back for 8200 years. It should be pointed out that really accurate tree-ring dating is not a simple matter. Sometimes rings or parts of rings are missing, or extremely narrow because of drought. However, if care is taken, tree-ring counting gives us an accurate absolute method of dating going back for 8200 years. That is its importance.

2.3 Was the world created in 4004 BC?

Since tree-ring dating goes back 8200 years we know beyond reasonable doubt that the world was *not* created in 4004 BC, as claimed by Bishop Ussher. Some creationists today still believe in the 4004 BC date, as did Sir Isaac Newton, one of the greatest scientists of all time. We can say with reasonable certainty that they are wrong.

Other creationists believe that the Earth's age is about 10 000 years, while evolutionists believe it is 4600 million years. To investigate these claims we obviously need a dating method that goes further back than tree-ring dating can.

2.4 The Radiocarbon Clock

The invention of the radiocarbon dating method caused a sensation, when it was announced by William F. Libby in New York in 1949. For the first time it seemed that fossils could be dated reliably and accurately. All that was needed was some laboratory equipment and a small piece of the fossil material, and a scientist could work out how old the fossil was. In this section we look at what radiocarbon dating is, and then consider whether the method really is as reliable and accurate as was thought.

For many people, the word 'radioactive' conjures up a picture of the mushroom cloud of an atomic bomb explosion. However, there are many useful applications of radioactivity, for example in the treatment of cancer, and the tracing of leaks in oil and gas pipes. We can also use radioactivity as an 'atomic clock' to date the past. How does this work?

The air we breathe contains mainly nitrogen and oxygen. It also contains small quantities of other gases, in particular 0.03% of carbon dioxide (CO_2). A very tiny fraction of the carbon atoms in carbon dioxide is radioactive carbon, called **radiocarbon** for short. In fact there is only one atom of radiocarbon for every million million atoms of normal carbon, in the carbon dioxide of the air.

As is well known, green plants take in carbon dioxide from the air, to make the carbon compounds they need for growth. In fact *all* the carbon in plants comes from the carbon dioxide in air. Animals in turn eat plants, or eat other animals that have eaten plants. So all the carbon in animals ultimately comes from the carbon dioxide in air too. Thus the carbon in the bodies of both plants and animals contains the same tiny proportion of radioactive carbon atoms as does the atmosphere.

Radioactive elements decay with age and turn into different elements, giving out **radiation** in the process. In particular radioactive carbon decays into nitrogen, giving out a type of radiation called β particles. The radiation can be detected and measured using a Geiger counter.

The important point about the decay is the rate at which it takes place. Suppose we start with 8 atoms of radiocarbon. After a certain length of time, called the half-life, on average half of these will have turned into nitrogen and there will be only 4 radiocarbon atoms left. After the same length of time again, half of these will have turned into nitrogen, and there will be only 2 radiocarbon atoms left. Libby, the inventor of radiocarbon dating, measured the half-life of radiocarbon as 5568 years. Thus, as shown in Box 4, if we start with a certain quantity of radiocarbon, after 5568 years on average only half of it will be left. After a further 5568 years only half of that will be left, and so on.

Box 4   Radiocarbon Dating

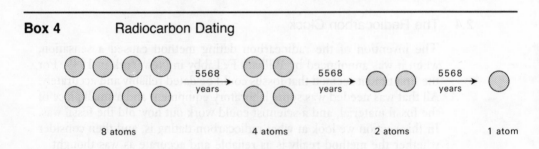

| 8 atoms | 4 atoms | 2 atoms | 1 atom |

When a plant or animal dies, it stops taking in carbon. The radiocarbon in it slowly decays. The proportion of radiocarbon to normal carbon in it therefore gets lower and lower. Scientists can measure the amount of radiocarbon in an old skull, for example, and compare it to the amount of normal carbon. They know the initial proportion when it was living—the same as in the atmosphere (assuming this has remained constant through time.) They also know the half-life of radiocarbon. Hence they can calculate the age of the skull.

2.5 Is radiocarbon dating reliable?

Is radiocarbon dating reliable? Most creationists say 'no'. But what are the facts? Historical dates we can be really sure of (for example the death of Julius Caesar) do not go back beyond about 1400 BC, surprising as this may seem. Radiocarbon dating fits the known historical dates reasonably well, back to about 1000 BC. To go further back in time we must compare radiocarbon dating with tree-ring dating. We can do this using the same tree. The first such comparison was made using bristlecone pines in 1966, and the results surprised many scientists. Radiocarbon dating was found to be not nearly as accurate as had been thought. For example trees dated at 4000 BC by the radiocarbon method were found to be about *1000 years older* (i.e. 5000 BC) using tree-ring counting. The main reason for the discrepancy is that the proportion of radiocarbon to normal carbon in the atmosphere has *not* remained constant with time. It is slowly and non-uniformly decreasing as time goes on. When scientists make their measurements, they must take this into account. (The reasons that the proportion of radioactive carbon in the atmosphere has not remained constant with time are complex. For example, changes in the earth's magnetic field with time affect the creation of radiocarbon in the atmosphere by cosmic rays.)

Radiocarbon dating can be used for only about the last 70 000 years. If the sample is older than this, there is not enough radiation left to measure. For older specimens, and in particular for dating old rocks, we can use radioactive forms of other elements such as uranium and potassium; these have a much longer half-life than radiocarbon. As with radiocarbon dating, each method has errors, but scientists can sometimes make cross-checks using different pairs of elements. Using cross-checks we find that radioactive dating methods *are* reliable, giving dates accurate to about ±10 per cent. This means that if a fossil is dated as 50 million years old, we can be fairly sure that its age is between 45 and 55 million years.

2.6 The Age of the Earth

Another place I visited while in Arizona was a giant meteorite crater, lying in the desert about 100 miles from the Grand Canyon. The crater is almost 1 mile across, 3 miles around the top and 570 feet deep. U.S. astronauts go there to practice landing on the Moon! Meteorites are fragments of interplanetary rock that fall to the Earth from time to time.

They are thought to be leftover bits of the material from which our solar system was formed. (Our solar system is the sun and its family of planets, including the Earth.) Scientists believe that our sun and its planets were all formed at about the same time: they were probably born after a massive explosion of a very bright star called a Supernova. Hence the Earth is believed to be the same age as the rest of the solar system.

How do we know the age of our solar system? When a meteorite hits the Earth and is recovered, scientists can measure its age using radioactive dating; normally radioactive uranium is used. By this method, the age of meteorites is found to be 4600 million years. We also know the age of the Moon from radioactive dating of samples of moonrock brought back by astronauts. The oldest moonrocks have been dated at 4600 million years too. Scientists therefore believe our solar system to be 4600 million years old.

The oldest rocks known on the Earth are 3900 million years old. Why not 4600 million years old? Scientists believe that the reason is that it took about 700 million years for the cloud of dust and gas that formed the 'proto-earth' to collapse into an Earth with a molton interior surrounded by a solid crust. Scientists date the age of the Earth from when it *started* to form, 4600 million years ago.

2.7   How old is Life on Earth?

When did life form on Earth? The earliest evidence comes from traces of the outlines of colonies of bacteria, in rocks around 3000 million years old. Sea snail fossils have been found which are 600 million years old. From fossils we also know that primitive fish lived 400 million years ago, dinosaurs 200 million years ago, and the first whales 50 million years ago. Man built the Pyramids in Egypt only 4500 years ago! We will give a more detailed account in Chapter 5 of when life developed.

As we have seen, the evidence is extremely strong that the Earth is 4600 million years old, and that different types of animals emerged at intervals of many millions of years. However, creationists believe the Earth is only 10 000 years old, or even less. How can they possibly believe this, in the face of all the evidence? They have three different answers. First, some creationists claim that radioactive dating is unreliable. But their evidence for this appears as shaky as that in Box 5 when examined in detail. Even if radioactive dates are wrong by as much as 50%, which is extremely unlikely, the Earth is still many millions of years old. Second, many creationists believe that fossil evidence from the Grand Canyon and other places can be explained away by a massive Genesis flood. Third, many believe in the theory of Apparent Age. We shall deal with these last two ideas below. (It should be pointed out here

that a small minority of creationists do believe the Earth to be very old.
We will look at their views later, on page 24.)

2.8 The Genesis Flood

How do creationists explain the layers of rocks containing fossils that
exist in the Grand Canyon, and all over the world? The major creationist
book on this subject is *The Genesis Flood*, a 500 page book written by
Morris and Whitcomb in 1961. Creationists argue that about 3000 years
before Christ there was a massive world-wide flood which lasted for
about a year. Huge waves travelled at a thousand miles an hour over the
surface of the flood waters, picking up animals and plants and carrying
them along. As the waves died down they deposited mud, animals and
plants. Under the tremendous pressure of the water the mud hardened
into layers of rock. Man, who fled to the highest hills, was caught last and
so is found in only the topmost layers of rock.

This is an ingenious theory. But what are the facts? First, there is *no*
scientific evidence that a massive world-wide flood occurred about 5000
years ago. Second, geologists have a good understanding of how rocks
are formed: the process takes vast periods of time, not just one year.
Third, we know from radioactive dating that the rocks and their fossils
were deposited over thousands of millions of years.

How do creationists react to all these arguments? They put forward
another ingenious theory: the theory of Apparent Age.

Box 5   **Did humans live alongside dinosaurs?**

About 10 years ago a film was made by creationists called *Footprints in Stone*.
This film has been, and is still being, screened throughout the world. It claims
to show footprints of men alongside those of dinosaurs at Paluxy Creek, Texas.
Creationists believe these prints to be prime evidence that man did not emerge
millions of years after dinosaurs became extinct, as claimed by evolutionists,
and hence that the evolutionary timescale is completely wrong.

At first sight the footprint pictures look plausible. There is no doubt that some
of the footprints are those of dinosaurs. However, there is a great deal of doubt
about the so-called 'human' footprints. For a start, these 'humans' had
footprints 21 inches long, and a 7 foot stride! The creationists argue that they
were giants and quote Genesis 6:4 'there were giants on the earth'. All of the
'human' footprints are eroded and of poor quality. Some have distinct claw
marks protruding from what creationists call the heel. Since the quality of the
prints is poor, the film makers apparently decided to 'highlight' the so-called
toes with oil and sand before filming!

The evidence that these footprints really are human is very weak. Indeed
some creationists are now sceptical about them and one, Dr Neufeld, has
suggested that they may have been chiselled out during the Depression to
increase tourism to Paluxy Creek!

2.9 The Creationist theory of Apparent Age

In 1857 Philip Henry Gosse published a book entitled *Omphalos; An attempt to Untie the Geological Knot*. *Omphalos* is the Greek word for navel. The navel is what remains when the umbilical cord is cut from a new-born baby. Did Adam have a navel, even though he was not born? Of course he did, said Gosse. God created him the way he meant all human beings to be. In the same way, the trees he created were fully grown trees with rings in them. Thus, Gosse argued, although the creation took place in 4004 BC, if we try to date it scientifically it appears older.

Modern creationists have updated this idea: see the quotation in Box 6. Thus many creationists accept the scientific evidence that the world appears to be very old, but they argue that it was *created* with this *appearance* of age only 6000 or 10 000 years ago.

Box 6   Creationist theory of apparent age

Let us imagine that Adam was a scientist interested in determining the age of the earth. He starts his research on the eighth day of creation, in and around the garden of Eden. He cuts down a tree in order to build a fire, and counts the growth rings. According to this, the earth is at least 139 years old. The next day he explores a canyon started 750 000 years ago by a river and marvels at the layers of rock, some formed almost 3000 million years in the past, according to his geological timescale, which is based upon rock formation phenomena. And so Adam, the scientist, determines that the age of the world is at least 3000 million years old—yet it is a world which was created just eight days earlier.

R. G. Korthals, *Scientific Studies in Special Creation*, 1971

Logically it is impossible to tell the difference between:
 i a world which really is very old
 ii a world which is young but has been given a perfect appearance of age.
However, sheer common sense suggests that (i) must be preferred to (ii). If science demonstrates that the earth is very old and that life has emerged over millions of years, then it is rather absurd to state that this is not the case. From a Christian point of view the God who created all of life is the same God as He who reveals His creation to us. God does not deceive us by leaving old fossils lying about! Our study of the world shows clearly that it is very old and that life has emerged over millions of years. It is therefore reasonable to conclude that this is the timescale over which God has created life on Earth.

2.10 Conclusion

We have shown that there is extremely strong evidence against creationism. In particular the creationist theory of a 'young Earth', up to 10 000 years old, cannot be correct. Having considered creationism, we are now ready to concentrate on investigating evolution. We will do that in the next chapter.

Questions for Discussion

2.1 In what way does the Grand Canyon tell us something about the past?

2.2 Explain why tree-ring counting is an accurate dating method

2.3 How it is possible to go back 8200 years using tree-ring dating, when the oldest living tree is less than 5000 years old?

2.4 Explain the radiocarbon dating method, in your own words. How reliable is this method?

2.5 What is the creationist theory of apparent age?

How did evolution occur?

3.1 What are fossils?

In the last chapter we disposed of the creationists' arguments. That leaves us with evolution. But how did evolution occur? Did life evolve by slow and gradual changes or by sudden jumps? Is Darwinism correct? To answer these questions we need to examine fossils more closely.

A most unusual expedition is being planned, even as I write this chapter. A group of biologists is preparing to travel to Siberia, to collect sperm from frozen mammoths. Mammoths are a type of elephant that became extinct about 30 000 years ago. They had very long tusks and, unlike our present elephants, were covered with long reddish-brown hair. Many complete mammoth bodies have been found preserved in the Siberian ice; in fact, cases have been reported of meat from frozen mammoth carcasses being used to feed sledge dogs. Some biologists believe the ice has preserved the mammoths so well that their sperm will still be active, once thawed out. The purpose of the expedition is to try to fertilise a modern female elephant with 30 000-year-old mammoth sperm to produce a mammoth/elephant baby. By the time you read this chapter you may have heard whether the expedition has been successful or not.

Fossils are the remains or traces of animals and plants, preserved from ancient times. Occasionally complete animals are preserved, as in the case of the mammoths. Often only their bones or shells are preserved. Or there may just be fossil tracks and footprints, or fossil plants, which are impressions of twigs and leaves in rocks. Preservation may have occurred in several ways. Both soft and hard body parts may be preserved by freezing, as with the mammoths. Usually only hard body parts, like shells and bones, are preserved, and frequently these have been 'fossilised' by the addition of mineral matter, so that the fossils are effectively made out of rock. Moulds and casts of animals and plants in rocks are also found; these are formed when the original remains dissolve away.

The vast majority of animals leave no trace of their existence when they die. Their flesh decays, and their bones turn to powder. It is only very occasionally that an animal becomes fossilised. For example, a land animal is likely to become fossilised only if it falls into water, where its flesh can rot away and its bones settle into mud. If the mud gets covered with layers of dead plants, then, after many centuries, the deposit may turn to peat, and later to coal, with the bones still embedded within. Eventually chemical changes in the bones turn them to rock, but they still retain the shape they had when living.

3.2   The fossil record

Well-preserved mummies show us what Egyptians looked like 4000 years ago. In a similar way fossils enable us to find out what animals and plants were like many millions of years ago. The history of life as revealed by fossils is called the **fossil record**. It wasn't until modern times that people started to realise the significance of fossils. Before then the fact that a piece of 'rock' looked like a shellfish, for example, was regarded as a fascinating coincidence. Some people even thought that God had decorated rocks with ornamental replicas of living things, in order to make them more interesting.

It is important to remember that most fossils are not nearly as complete as the frozen mammoths or Egyptian mummies, and so we must expect some difficulties in reconstructing ancient animals and plants. In addition, only a small fraction of the animals that die become preserved as fossils, and only a tiny proportion of these will lie near the surface of rocks. The fossil record is therefore very incomplete.

How is the fossil record built up? First the fossils have to be found, either by dedicated fossil hunters or by chance discovery. Then they have to be dated, using the radioactive dating methods described in Chapter 2. Radioactive dating requires a skilled scientist. However anyone can date fossils relative to each other, if they are found in rocks that lie in undisturbed layers. Fossils found in the lower layers must be older than those in the upper layers, so it is easy to arrange the finds in order of age.

3.3   The fossil evidence

We would expect the fossil record to provide answers to the following questions:
  i What were the stages in the development of plants and animals?
 ii Is there evidence for evolution on a small scale—for example changes in the shape of oyster shells?
iii Is there evidence for evolution on a large scale—for example reptiles turning into birds?
 iv Was evolution gradual and continuous, or were there sudden jumps?
We have already partially answered the first question, in chapter 2. There is strong evidence from the fossil record that the main order of appearance of animals has been:

1 Single-celled animals (e.g. bacteria)
2 Multi-celled invertebrates (e.g. jelly fish)
3 Fishes with backbones
4 Amphibians living in water and on land
5 Reptiles (including dinosaurs)
6 Birds and mammals

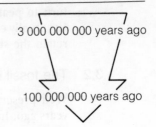

3 000 000 000 years ago

100 000 000 years ago

The fossil record shows a similar succession for plants.

We can therefore reasonably conclude from the fossil record that more complex forms of life have emerged successively. The next question is 'How did that happen?'. First we ask if there is any evidence that evolution on a small scale has occurred: biologists call this **micro-evolution**.

3.4 Evolution on a small scale

Each year many new varieties of roses are produced by rose breeders, with only small changes from one variety to the next. The changes are the result of small-scale evolution, brought about by the artificial selection and breeding of those plants with better flowers. Likewise, the fossil record contains many thousands of examples of small changes in, say, the shapes of oyster shells. Most creationists accept that these changes are also the result of small-scale evolution, so do not disagree with evolutionists on this point.

As you saw on page 6, Darwin called the mechanism by which he thought evolution occurred *natural selection*, as distinct from artificial selection by plant and animal breeders. It is useful to consider a modern example of how natural selection works.

How a white moth turned black

When I was a boy I used to collect and breed butterflies and moths. I vividly remember chasing over chalk hills in the day time, waving a butterfly net, and painting tree trunks at night time with a mixture of molasses and rum. Moths would be attracted by the smell, drink the rum cocktail, and then fall to the ground in a drunken state. Using a torch it was easy to pick out the desired species of moth. By morning these would have recovered from their hangover, and would happily breed.

One of the moths I still have in my collection is a black-winged moth called the peppered moth (*Biston betularia*). Had I been collecting 100 years earlier, this same peppered moth would almost certainly have had silvery-white wings. I know this from a naturalists' survey of 1849, which

20

showed that about 99% of peppered moths had whitish wings and only a rare 1% had black wings. Why and how did the white wings become black? The answer is simple. In the first half of the nineteenth century, a white peppered moth would have been well camouflaged by the lichen that grew on the tree trunks where it rested during the day. A black one, on the other hand, would have been easily seen and eaten by passing birds. During the second half of the century, however, the situation changed. In industrial areas the lichen was killed off, and tree-trunks blackened, by soot and other pollutants from the new factories, mills and metalworks that burned coal fuel. The white moth was no longer camouflaged, and stood out clearly from its resting place, while the black one remained hidden, and survived. The result was that by 1900, in industrial areas, 98% of peppered moths had black wings, compared with the 1% in 1849. Biologists call this phenomenon *industrial melanism*, because the black-winged moths contain extra melanin pigment in their wings. Industrial melanism is known to have occurred in hundreds of different insects in Britain, North America and Europe.

Today we have strict laws against air pollution. The air is now cleaner, so lichen is on the increase again. And so is the original whitish variety of the moth, since it is now the variety better camouflaged to survive. This is a striking example of natural selection in action. The animals and plants that prosper are those that are best adapted: in the case of the peppered moth, it is the form that is better camouflaged.

It is clear, therefore, that small-scale evolution *can* occur by Darwin's mechanism of natural selection. However it is important to note that no *new* type of peppered moth was produced in this case. Only the *ratio* of white to black forms changed dramatically.

But can completely new variations occur? In 1791 an American, Seth White, noticed that an unusual ram had been born on his farm; it was a ram with very short legs. Seth used the ram for breeding, and found that two of its offspring also had very short legs. By breeding these together, Seth eventually produced a whole flock of short-legged sheep. The sheep became known as the Ancon breed. They were very popular among farmers, who no longer needed such high fences around their farms, and could therefore save money on fence materials. The original ram's short legs were caused by a **genetic mutation**, which is a change in the structure of a **gene**. (You will learn more about genes in the next chapter.) Usually such mutations are harmful. But occasionally the mutation is an improvement, enabling the offspring to be more successful than its parent. Seth was lucky—his ram's short legs were due to a much larger mutation than usual, and Seth was able to select and breed this desirable feature.

Can *natural* selection acting on mutations explain the evolution of new species? Darwin thought that it could, and it certainly seems to explain convincingly the origin of the finch species mentioned in Chapter 1.

The fossil record gives much evidence for small-scale evolution, and we have shown, using modern examples, that such micro-evolution can be explained by Darwin's theory of natural selection. We must now ask whether the fossil record gives evidence for large-scale evolution occurring too.

3.5 Evolution on a large scale

Evolution on a large scale is called **macroevolution**. An example would be the change from reptiles to birds. Did such a change really take place? And if so, how? At first sight we would expect the fossil record to answer these questions. However, the quotation in Box 7 shows that Darwin himself was well aware of the huge gaps in the fossil record. Even so, he was confident that subsequent fossil findings would fill the gaps, and that eventually a complete record of macroevolution would exist. But has this in fact happened?

Box 7   Darwin and Fossils

The number of intermediate varieties, which have formerly existed on earth, must be truly enormous. Why then is not every geological formation and every stratum full of such intermediate links? Geology assuredly does not reveal any such finely graduated organic chain; and this, perhaps, is the most obvious and gravest objection which can be urged against my theory.

Charles Darwin, *The Origin of Species*, 1859

Since Darwin's time we *have* found an enormous number of fossils. In the world's museums there are now about 250 000 different species of fossil plants and animals. If Darwin was correct, these should contain a great many transitional or intermediate forms. Creationists argue strongly that there are none. Some evolutionists believe there are thousands, while others admit there are still significant gaps (see Box 8).

Box 8   Are there gaps in the Fossil Record?

There are literally thousands of transitional forms, and more are discovered every year.
G. L. Stebbins (an evolutionist), in *Biological Sciences Curriculum Study Newsletter*, 1972

The fossil record is rather full of gaps.
Niles Eldredge (an evolutionist), *The Monkey Business*, 1982

There are enormous gaps in the fossil record.
A. J. Monty White (a creationist), *What About Origins?* 1978

Most evolutionists would agree that one of the clearest examples of an intermediate fossil is **Archaeopteryx**. This fossil, at first sight half-bird/half-reptile, was discovered in a slab of limestone in Bavaria in 1860, a year after *The Origin of Species* was published. Since then a number of other *Archaeopteryx* fossils have been found. The facts about *Archaeopteryx* are given in Box 9.

Box 9   Half-bird/Half-reptile

Archaeopteryx lived about 150 million years ago. It had two characteristics usually associated with reptiles: teeth and a bony tail. It also had reptile-like claws on its wings. The skeleton of the first specimen found looked so much like a reptile it was displayed as a 'flying reptile' in a Dutch museum. Scientists now classify it as a bird because it had feathers on its wings, and in fact the name *Archaeopteryx* means 'ancient feather'. *Archaeopteryx* is called an intermediate between reptiles and birds because it possesses characteristics common to both.

Until recently *Archaeopteryx* fossils were dated as being 60 million years older than the first birds, and for this reason some popular biology books regarded *Archaeopteryx* as the actual 'link' between reptiles and birds. However, in 1977, a fossil that was clearly a bird was discovered in Colorado, and dated to be as old as *Archaeopteryx*. *Archaeopteryx* is therefore *not* the actual ancestor of birds, but it *does* contain features common to both birds and reptiles. For this reason scientists believe that birds evolved from reptiles, although the *actual* links have yet to be found in the fossil record.

Archaeopteryx is an example of an intermediate between reptiles and birds. There are also intermediates between reptiles and mammals, called mammal-like reptiles. Scientists have found a series of reptile fossils which become more and more mammal-like, for example showing a change from simple reptilian teeth to the more complex array of grinding and cutting teeth possessed by mammals. Unfortunately the hallmarks of mammals—warm blood, hair and milk-producing breasts do not fossilise. Scientists can therefore only infer when these features started to appear. They cannot yet say with any confidence that particular fossils represent the actual links between reptiles and mammals, although there are many fossils which do show features common to both species (as does the present-day duck-billed platypus.)

We have considered above two examples of large scale evolution: from reptiles to birds and from reptiles to mammals. In general, the fossil record does *not* usually show a gradual transition from one form to another. Instead it indicates that a species remains the same for many millions of years and then, suddenly, it is replaced by a different related species. The many large gaps in the fossil record, as Darwin himself realised, present a serious objection to his theory. Darwin believed the process of evolution was gradual and continuous: it did not consist of sudden changes. The fossil record appears to rule this out. We will therefore now consider three newer theories that have been put forward: modified creationism, localised Darwinism, and fast evolution.

3.6 Three newer theories of evolution

1 Modified Creationism

Most creationists believe that creation occurred in literally 6 days, 6000 or 10 000 years ago. We have already shown them to be wrong. Some creationists however do believe in an old earth, and also in small-scale evolution. They argue that *large-scale* evolution has not occurred, and that God separately created all the *major* types of plants and animals. They claim that the fossil evidence is consistent with this viewpoint. However, although there are many gaps in the fossil record, there *are* some examples of intermediates. It is not very reasonable to suppose that the intermediates were specially created, one after the other. We therefore rule out modified creationism too.

2 Localised Darwinism

Recently I travelled to a very small town called Arthur, in Illinois, North America, to see the Amish people. The Amish live without electricity, television, telephones or cars, in only a few isolated communities in America. They have a characteristic form of dress: the women wear bonnets and the men have beards and broadbrimmed black hats. Usually

24

they marry only among themselves. The vast majority of visitors to America are completely unaware of their existence: if you travel through America at random the chances of coming across the Amish are very small indeed.

Let us imagine a major catastrophe in America, such as a series of gigantic earthquakes, which cuts off electricity, food supplies, and so on. The Amish people are used to living without air-conditioning and central heating, and support themselves on their own farms. They would survive this catastrophe much better than the average American. If the Amish were militant (which they are not) they might even be able to exterminate 'normal' Americans after the event.

Many biologists believe that evolution happened in just this sort of way. In some geographically isolated area, such as an island, or a valley cut off by mountains, an animal or plant started to develop differently. Interbreeding in its small community helped these differences to develop, until gradually a new local race was produced. If the new form was better adapted than the original one, the new race could 'take over' when it came into contact with the larger world. Since, according to this theory, evolutionary changes develop only in small isolated communities, the chance of coming across evidence of intermediate forms in the fossil record is very small. Scientists have given the name '*neo-Darwinism*' to this theory of localised evolution.

3 Fast evolution

Imagine that you wake up one morning to find your bicycle tyre has gone flat. It could have happened gradually (for example because of a leaking valve), or rapidly (because of a large puncture in the tube). Similarly evolution might occur slowly and gradually (as Darwin believed), or rapidly (as proposed recently by some biologists). This latter theory is called the theory of *punctuated equilibrium*. It supposes that species existed for millions of years in 'equilibrium' with their surroundings, changing very little. Then, suddenly, like a puncture, changes happened very rapidly, and in a small number of generations a new species emerged.

The chance of finding a given fossil depends on how long the species existed. The longer it existed, the more fossils will be buried in the earth. However if evolutionary changes happened very rapidly, the number of intermediate fossils would be small, and the chances of finding them even smaller. If the rapid changes also occurred in a geographically isolated community, the chances of finding intermediate fossils would be very slim indeed. This theory is consistent with the gaps in the fossil record.

Why should a species exist unchanged for many millions of years and then suddenly change? Why did dinosaurs reign for 150 million years and then become extinct 65 million years ago? Why did Ammonites (a type of shell fish) last for 330 million years, and end at the same time as the dinosaurs? There are various theories for this sudden extinction of species, and some scientists believe that the meteorite crater described on page 13f provides a clue.

Scientific computations indicate that giant meteorites, about 10 km in diameter, hit the earth every 50 million years or so. The impact would generate about 10^{23} Joules of energy: this is 100 million times larger than that of a megaton bomb (the energy of one million tonnes of TNT). If the meteorite happened to hit the ocean it would create enormous waves. If it hit land it would throw up a huge cloud of dust, large enough to black out all sunlight for several months over much of the Earth. Catastrophes like giant meteorites could be responsible for the sudden extinction of the dinosaurs, and the rapid changes in the environment could lead to the fast evolutionary changes indicated by the fossil record.

Biologists are actively, and sometimes heatedly, debating which theory, neo-Darwinism or punctuated equilibrium, better fits the fast changes in the fossil record. The key question is, just how fast did species change? Neo-Darwinists believe that the fast changes indicated by the fossil record are not too fast to be explained by a series of small changes (mutations) acted upon by natural selection. On the other hand, some believers in punctuated equilibrium maintain that the changes were so fast that a new mechanism of evolution is required. Which theory is correct? Scientists need a more detailed fossil record to answer that, and also a better understanding of genetics. In the next chapter we look at genes and brains and the evidence they give for evolution, and we also consider the evolution of our own species, man.

Questions for Discussion

3.1   What are fossils? Give three examples.

3.2   Try to find two examples of artificial selection in *animals*, and explain why it has been carried out.

3.3   What is the fossil evidence for:
      i evolution on a small scale?
      ii evolution on a large scale?

3.4   If Darwin were alive today, do you think he would believe in Darwinism? Give reasons for your answer.

3.5   Describe two newer theories of evolution which seem to fit the fossil evidence.

26

4   Genes, Brains, and the Origin of Man

I have a school textbook before me with an illustration showing the evolution of man. On the left is drawn a hairy ape-like figure; on the right is a clean-shaven modern man; in the middle is a near-man with 3 days growth of beard! But is the illustration correct? In this chapter we look at the evidence for how man developed. First we look at the two most important ingredients of man: genes and brains.

4.1   The Genetic Code

Your body is made up of about one hundred million cells. Nearly every cell contains a complete package of hereditary instructions for the individual that is you. They are to be found in two sets of **chromosomes**, one set taken from your mother's egg and the other from your father's sperm.

Each chromosome contains a very long molecule of a chemical called DNA (which stands for DeoxyriboNucleic Acid.) The DNA molecule consists of strings of four different chemical units called **nucleotides**. It is usually coiled up into a double helix to save space. Each DNA molecule is subdivided into **genes**, and these are the units of inherited material. A gene is therefore a section, or several separated sections, of DNA. Each gene contains thousands of nucleotides.

Just as dots and dashes spell out a message in Morse code, so the order in which the nucleotides are joined together spells out the gene's message, in what is called the **genetic code**. Whether a particular cell will form part of, say, an ankle bone, or skin on the end of a finger, depends on which of its genes are 'switched on'—a process which scientists do not yet understand. An eminent biologist, Richard Dawkins, has called we humans 'gene machines'.

It is important to realise that the *same* four chemical units make up the DNA of *all* living things. Many (though not all) biologists regard this as evidence of a single ancestor to all of life, since otherwise they would expect to find many different types of DNA molecule with various numbers of different chemical units. It is as if the plans for building and maintaining the whole living world (bacteria, grass, elephants, humans, and so on) are written out in a four-letter alphabet. An alphabet with only four letters might seem to be very limited. But computers are based on an even shorter 'alphabet' with only two characters (0 and 1), and we all know how powerful modern computers can be. Similarly Morse code is based on only two characters, a dot and a dash.

4.2 Genes and Evolution

If I wanted to transmit just this sentence using Morse Code, I would need only a short length of code. But if I wanted to transmit this whole book, a very long length of code would be required. Scientists can measure the length of the genetic code in the chromosomes of organisms. They have found that its active length increases in going from bacteria to algae to amphibia to reptiles to man. That sequence agrees with our view of the increasing complexity of these animals. It is also identical to the order in which the animals appear in the fossil record. This strongly suggests that animals have evolved, and become more complex, by increasing the amount of information stored in their genes.

How long is the genetic code in man? It is typically the same length as in other mammals. Thus, as regards the amount of information contained in our genes, we are very similar to other mammals.

4.3 The Brain

In what ways do we differ from other animals? We have higher intelligence, good memories, moral awareness, and so on. All these things are due to our superior brains. Most animals are born with their brains fully developed. In humans, however, the brain at birth is only a quarter of its final size: it goes on growing for about 25 years, rapidly at first and then more slowly. A very important result of this is that humans are out in the world while their brains are still growing, which means they can learn and adapt to a changing environment.

Of all the animals, humans do *not* have the largest brains. Whales, elephants and dolphins all have greater brain masses than man. However these large animals also have much more body to control than man. As a rough guide to intelligence, biologists sometimes use the brain–mass/body–mass ratio. Using this, man comes top of the intelligence league, followed by the dolphin. It is interesting to note that the brain of an average woman is about 150 cubic centimetres smaller than that of an average man. But before male readers of this book start to celebrate, remember that women tend to be smaller and lighter than men—the brain–mass/body– mass ratio is about the same for both sexes!

The brain–mass/body–mass ratio is only a crude guide to intelligence. Scientists believe that a better guide is to look at the *complexity* of the brain—for example the number of brain cells and the number of connections between them. When this is done humans come top of the league, followed by other mammals, then reptiles, and then amphibians.

28

As with genes, a detailed study of the brains of animals shows a progression that matches the order of appearance of the animals in the fossil record. Therefore what we learn from the study of genes, brains and fossils is all consistent. It indicates not only that evolution occurred, but also the order in which it occurred.

4.4   The development of man

The question of who was, and who was not, an actual ancestor of man is still being hotly debated by scientists. Even as I write this chapter, the famous fossil hunter Richard Leakey is claiming that his latest fossil finds mean that the textbooks will have to be rewritten yet again.

How do we define man? It used to be thought that defining man as 'the tool-maker' was sufficient to distinguish him from the apes. However it has been found recently that modern chimpanzees can make crude tools out of wood and bone, so that definition will not do!

The earliest creature that made crude tools out of stones and bones is called *Australopithecus*, meaning 'Southern ape', because he was found in Africa and is classed as an ape. Many fossils of *Australopithecus* have been found, the oldest being about 6 million years old. Not only have we found skeletons and tools of *Australopithecus*, we have also found footprints, which show that he walked upright on two legs. Scientists are not agreed upon whether *Australopithecus* was or was not a direct ancestor of man. He had a brain size only about one-third the size of the human brain today.

The earliest fossils classified as man (*Homo*) are almost 4 million years old and the specimen they represent is called *Homo habilis*. He had a higher forehead and a larger brain than *Australopithecus*, he made better stone tools and walked well on two legs. Circular arrangements of stones found near *Homo habilis* skeletons probably indicate that he built crude huts.

Homo habilis died out, and *Homo erectus* emerged, about 1.5 million years ago. He had a larger brain than *Homo habilis*, made a great variety of stone tools and was the first man to use fire: scientists have found the remains of camp fires near *Homo erectus* skeletons. Then *Homo erectus* died out and our own species, *Homo sapiens* (meaning 'man the wise') emerged about 400 000 years ago. *Homo sapiens* had a still larger brain size.

The actual, or possible, ancestors of man are listed in Box 10. Within each species there is a range of brain sizes, as shown in the box. Nearly all scientists are agreed that *Homo erectus* was the immediate ancestor of *Homo sapiens*, and *Homo habilis* was probably the immediate ancestor of *Homo erectus*.

Box 10   The emergence of Man

Species	Age of Earliest Fossil (in years)	Brain Volume (in cubic centimeters)
Australopithecus (several species)	6 000 000	400– 600
Homo habilis	4 000 000	500– 800
Homo erectus	1 500 000	700–1200
Homo sapiens	400 000	1100–2200

The next major advance in man's history occurred only about 10 000 years ago. It was then that man gave up living as a hunter, and started to grow plants and breed animals for food. This meant he began to live in one place and form settled communities. The first settlements started 10 000 years ago in the Fertile Crescent—a crescent shaped region of land stretching from Israel and Jordan, north through Lebanon and parts of Syria, up to Turkey, and then curving down south-east through parts of Iraq and Iran to finish in Bahrein. I visited an archaelogical dig in Bahrein a few years ago and was proudly shown what were claimed to be the oldest lavatories in the world—two stone slabs with round holes roughly cut through them!

4.5   The uniqueness of man

Is man unique? At first sight the theory of evolution says no: in terms of intelligence there is simply a continuous progression of animals up the evolutionary tree, with man at the top. However, most Christians believe that man is unique, for reasons you can read in Chapter 6. But what are the scientific facts?

Genetically, man is similar to other mammals. Our closest relative is the chimpanzee, who is almost human in some respects. We probably enjoy watching chimps as much as we do because they remind us of someone we know! Genetically, chimpanzees and ourselves are astonishingly similar—about 99 per cent of the chimp's genetic material is the same as our own.

However, many biologists believe we humans *are* unique because of our *brain*. Although chimps and humans are very similar genetically, there is a large difference between the size of a chimp's brain, about 400 cubic centimetres, and that of modern man, typically 1400 cubic centimetres. It is not just the difference in size that is important: the human brain is also very much more complex, with many more connections between brain cells.

What seems to have happened is that, at some late stage in the evolution of the human brain, a level of complexity was reached which allowed the development of speech, moral awareness, high intelligence, learning, memory, understanding, and the other distinctive characteristics of man. The early ancestors of man then died out leaving an enormous gap, in terms of speech, consciousness, and so on, between modern man and other living animals. Thus many scientists believe that modern man is unique in today's world.

Questions for Discussion

4.1   What is meant by the *genetic code*?

4.2   Why do many scientists believe that all life has a single origin?

4.3   Explain how the study of genes and brains supports the theory of evolution.

4.4   What species were probably the ancestors of modern man, and how do their brain sizes compare with ours?

4.5   Make up your own list of features that distinguish humans from chimpanzees. (For example, humans farm but chimps don't.)

4.6   Do you think man is unique? Or do you think he is basically the same as other animals? Give reasons for your answer.

5   The Cosmic Calendar

5.1   How old is old?

We have shown that life on earth evolved over millions of years. The Earth itself is about 4600 million years old. It is important that we try to grasp how enormous a time period this is.

It is easy to understand one year of time, the interval between birthdays. Remembering life 10 years ago is also easy for most of us. An interval of 100 years is harder to appreciate, although many of us will know people who are 70, 80, 90 or even 100 years old. 1000 years of time is difficult to imagine; it takes us back beyond the Battle of Hastings (1066). But 1000 million years is vast. How can we begin to grasp what it means?

One way is to try counting from 1 to 1000 million. How long would that take? Counting fast I can count from 1 to 200 in one minute. At this rate, assuming I could keep it up and did not stop for food, drink, sleep, work, or anything else, it would take me 10 years to count from 1 to 1000 million. It would take nearly 50 years, non-stop, to count to the age of the Earth.

Geographers have a good way of thinking about large *distances*. They draw scale maps. This way, a map of the whole world can be drawn on a single sheet of paper. The best way to get an idea of millions of years is to make a scale drawing in *time*. We will go back as far as the creation of the Universe, and we will call this time-map the **cosmic calendar**. But first we will consider how and when the Universe began.

5.2   The Origin of the Universe

Gaze up into the sky on a clear night and you will see hundreds of bright, white stars. Many more stars become visible through a telescope, and it is found that the light from them becomes redder the further they are away. Scientists call this effect the 'red shift'. The reason for it is that light reaching us from distant stars has longer wavelength (shifted towards the red end of the spectrum) and hence lower frequency than light from nearer stars.

The red shift is the key to determining the age of the Universe. We can understand why by considering a Red Cross ambulance! Imagine an ambulance rushing towards you with its siren blaring. The noise has a higher pitch as the ambulance approaches than it has as the ambulance speeds away again. The siren is, of course, sending out the same musical notes all the time. But when the ambulance is travelling fast towards you the sound waves get 'squashed up', and therefore strike your ear with a higher frequency; when it is leaving you the sound waves get 'stretched out', and hit your ear with a lower frequency. By the same reasoning, since the light from distant stars has been 'stretched out' to lower frequencies, these stars must be speeding away from us. By measuring the amount of the red shift, astronomers can determine the speed of the stars. They have found that the more distant the stars are, the greater is the red shift, and hence the faster these stars are travelling away from us. We are living in an expanding Universe.

Imagine going back in time, and running the Universe backwards, so that it contracts. The stars which are now far away will move closer and closer, as we go further and further back. Using this argument, if we go back far enough, we should find that everything was once squeezed into one 'lump', a dense concentration of matter and energy. Scientists calculate that this was the case about 15 000 million years ago, and that the lump exploded, blasting particles and energy out through space to form the Universe. This theory of the origin of the Universe is often called the **Big Bang theory**. It is the point to which scientists can trace events as of now. It was not necessarily the very first moment of existence—scientists do not yet know whether anything existed before the Big Bang. Christians believe that God created the first matter and energy; for Christians, if there was nothing before the Big Bang, then the Big Bang marks the start of the Creation.

After the Big Bang, matter concentrated into hot glowing lumps (stars) which clustered together into groups called galaxies. Some of the stars in turn exploded. Our own galaxy, of which our solar system is a part, contains about 100 000 million stars. You saw in chapter two that our solar system is thought to have been formed about 4600 million years ago, from the explosion of a very bright star called a Supernova. So just as life on Earth appears to have developed by a process of evolution from simple cells, the Earth itself appears to have evolved from the original Big Bang. It seems that evolution is the general way in which God chose to work.

5.3   The Origin of Life

Where did the original living cells come from? First we need to answer the question 'What is a living thing?'. The simplest way to distinguish living from non-living things is that living things can reproduce—they can make copies of themselves. This definition is not foolproof. For example a crystal of salt or sugar will grow in its own saturated solution, and if it breaks in half two similar crystals will be formed. However, apart from such cases as this, the ability to reproduce is the most useful simple definition of a living thing.

The most widely accepted biological theory of the origin of life is the 'primeval soup' theory. This theory proposes that the early atmosphere of the earth contained simple molecules, such as hydrogen, ammonia and methane molecules (which were emitted during volcanic eruptions), and carbon dioxide and nitrogen molecules. Lightning flashes and sunlight caused those simple molecules to combine into larger, more complex ones. These dissolved in the oceans, and in hot volcanic pools, forming a thin 'chemical soup'. Evaporation caused the soup to become more concentrated. Then lightning flashes and radioactive emission from rocks caused the molecules in the soup to assemble into more complex substances: proteins and amino acids. Eventually molecules that could reproduce themselves appeared—'living molecules' such as DNA.

The primeval soup theory is plausible, but we do not yet know if that really is the way life developed. Parts of the theory have been tested in a laboratory. For example scientists have mixed molecules of hydrogen, ammonia, methane, carbon dioxide, nitrogen and water in a flask, and subjected them to electrical discharges. More complex molecules were indeed formed, including some of the amino acids that are present in proteins. But no one has yet come close to forming a molecule which reproduces itself, because the probability that this will happen by chance in a flask of chemicals is extremely small.

Some scientists believe that the chance of life having evolved on earth in this way is so small as to be negligible. For example, Sir Fred Hoyle has stated that the probability of a living molecule being assembled 'by accident' out of simple molecules is lower than the probability of a hurricane sweeping through a scrap-metal yard and assembling a jumbo jet. This has prompted some scientists to propose that life originated elsewhere in the vastness of space, and that the living molecules came to Earth on comets or meteorities. However, most biologists do believe that life originated on Earth, even though the details of the process are not yet known.

Creationists claim to have the answer. They maintain that the Bible teaches that living things cannot develop from non-living things. In fact the Bible does not teach this, as you will see in the next chapter. And it is interesting to note that, from the time of the ancient Greeks until at least the Middle Ages, everyone, including Christians, believed in the 'spontaneous generation' of life from non-living materials. For example, it was thought that maggots were formed from dead meat and frogs from damp mud. Christians should therefore have no difficulty, in principle, in believing that living molecules can be produced from simple non-living ones.

5.4 The Cosmic Calendar

You saw that the universe was probably formed in a 'Big Bang' about 15 000 million years ago. In our cosmic calendar we will represent this length of time by one year, so that the scale of the map is 1:15 000 000 000. In other words, one day on the calendar is equivalent to 15 000 000 000 days of real time, or about 42 million years.

The origin of the universe, the Big Bang, took place on 1st January, according to this calendar. Today is represented by midnight on the 31st December. Some important pre-December dates in the calendar are listed in Box 11. They are the best estimates obtained by scientists, using a variety of dating methods. However, as noted in Chapter Two, these dates are approximate. For example, we may well be wrong by millions of years about when life first appeared on earth.

Box 11   Cosmic Calendar: pre-December dates

Scale: 1 day = 42 million years

Big Bang	January 1
Origin of our solar system	September 9
Formation of the earth	September 14
Origin of life on earth	September 25
Oldest fossils (bacteria and algae)	October 9
First cells with nuclei	November 15

Pause and try to imagine the enormous span of time, thousands of millions of years, from the Big Bang until the first cells were formed. It wasn't until 16 December—that is 600 million years ago—that the first worms appeared. From then on, so much happened that we need a daily calendar. See Box 12.

Box 12 **The first animals and plants**
Cosmic Calendar   14–31 December
Scale: 1 day = 42 million years

Sunday	Monday	Tuesday	Wednesday	Thursday	Friday	Saturday
14	15	16 worms	17	18	19 fish vertebrates	20
21 insects	22 amphibians	23 trees reptiles	24 dinosaurs	25	26 mammals	27 birds
28 flowers	29 primates	30 hominids	31 humans			

What I find really staggering, on this time scale, is that the first dinosaurs appeared as late as Christmas Eve! The first men and women appear on the very last day of the year, 31 December. The exact time depends on how we define 'human'. According to one definition, they appear at about 10.30 p.m. on 31 December, that is about 2½ million years ago. All of recorded history, about the last 5000 years, occupies only the last 10 seconds of 31 December, on the cosmic calendar.

The cosmic calendar should make us feel very humble. For most of the time the universe has existed, there has been neither man nor woman. We occupy just a tiny speck of time on one out of millions of planets. The cosmic calendar also suggests, however, that we are very special, at the top of the ladder of life. It has taken an immense journey through time to produce us. Christians believe that God is the Master Mind who planned this great journey, and that we are indeed something special.

Questions for Discussion

5.1   What is the Big Bang theory?

5.2   Describe the most widely accepted biological theory of the origin of life.

5.3   List the order in which the main types of animals appeared, according to fossil dating. (For this you will need to turn back to Chapter 3.)

5.4   Beside each animal listed in your answer to question 3, write down how long ago, in millions of years, it appeared. You can work this out using the cosmic calendar and the scale: *1 day = 42 million years*.

6   Genesis

6.1   Science and Christianity

The first five chapters of this book have been mainly concerned with science. However, it is important to remember that scientists look at the world from a particular point of view. Have you ever seen a set of architect's drawings of a building? There will be drawings of the building as seen from the sides, and from above, as well as sections through it at different levels. Each drawing is complete in itself. Yet all of them together are needed to describe the whole building.

Science represents one view of the building of truth, Christianity another. How do the views differ? Science mainly asks 'How?' For example, 'How did humans arrive on earth?' Christianity mainly asks 'Why?' For example, 'Why are we here?' Since truth is a unity, both the scientific and Christian views must be consistent. If they are not, then something is wrong with our understanding of science, or of Christianity, or of both. The evolution/creationism controversy arises because some people's understanding is wrong.

6.2   Understanding the Bible

Christians believe that God has shown us what He is like in a number of different ways: through Jesus, the Bible, the universe, and men and women through the ages. Christians believe the Bible is God's word to us, written by men in their own language and style.

The basic question to ask in understanding the Bible (or indeed any book) is 'What did the author mean?' It is helpful to realise that the Bible is a collection of different types of books: books of law, history, prophecy, poetry and letters. Some parts of it are meant to be understood literally. Other parts, for example the parables of Jesus, are stories meant to convey deeper truths. In most cases it is clear whether or not the author intended his words to be understood literally. In some cases, for example the Genesis creation account, it is not particularly clear. The interpretation of Genesis lies at the root of the evolution/creationism controversy.

6.3   The Genesis Account of Creation

We do not know who wrote Genesis, and there is nothing in the book itself to indicate its author. Whoever he was, he probably compiled

Genesis from earlier writings and family records. Various historians, for example Josephus, a famous Jewish historian born a few years after the crucifixion of Christ, state that Moses was the author. If this is correct, then Genesis was written in about 1250 BC, corresponding to the late Bronze Age and early Iron Age period in Palestine.

Box 13   Extracts from Genesis

In the beginning, God created the heavens and the earth.

And God said 'Let there be light', and there was light. God saw that the light was good, and he separated the light from the darkness. God called the light 'day' and the darkness he called 'night'. And there was evening, and there was morning—the first day.

And God said, 'Let the water teem with living creatures, and let birds fly above the earth across the expanse of sky'. So God created the great creatures of the sea and every living and moving thing with which the water teems, according to their kinds, and every winged bird, according to its kind.

Then God said 'Let us make man in our image, in our likeness, and let them rule over the fish of the sea and the birds of the air, over the livestock, over all the earth, and over all the creatures that move along the ground'.

God saw all that he had made, and it was very good. And there was evening and there was morning—the sixth day.

Thus the heavens and the earth were completed in all their vast array.

We quote some of the Genesis account of creation in Box 13. It is popularly believed that until the time of Charles Darwin, all Christians took Genesis to be literally true. That is not so. Although many Christians did interpret Genesis literally, there is plenty of evidence to show that many Christians (and Jews) did not. In fact the interpretation of Genesis has caused controversy for many centuries. Box 14 gives quotations from Origen, a third-century Christian Church Father, and Josephus, the first-century Jewish historian referred to above. From these it is clear that, from an early date, the Genesis creation account has also been interpreted figuratively.

How can we tell whether the author of Genesis intended his creation story to be taken literally or not? The following are clues:

i Part of the account is in metaphorical language. For example 'the tree of life' (*Gen. 3:22*). An identical phrase is used in the last book of the Bible, Revelation, again metaphorically. A literal tree is obviously not intended.

ii Some of the story is obviously symbolic. For example, there is a serpent that talks.

Box 14   Early views of Genesis

> Who that has understanding will regard the statement as truthful that the first three days existed without Sun, Moon and stars; and the first day without even a sky? And who is so ignorant as to suppose that God planted a real tree in Eden such that anyone eating of it with bodily teeth should obtain life, and eating of another tree should come to the knowledge of good and evil? No one, I think, can doubt that these things are related figuratively, not literally, in Scripture, and some mystical meaning may be indicated by it.
> Origen (Third Century AD) *De Principiis* IV, i, 5.
>
> Moses speaks some things wisely, yet enigmatically, and others allegorically.
> Josephus (First Century AD), *Antiquities of the Jews*, Preface, 4.

iii The whole account may be a description of a series of visions, the six days of creation being six days of visions. This would explain the curious repeated phrase 'and there was evening and there was morning. . . .'.

iv At the end of the 'six days' the writer clearly intends us to visualise a complete universe, with animals, trees and man, all much more than six days old.

v The writer deliberately and carefully chose the Hebrew word 'adam' meaning 'representative man' instead of the personal name of a particular man. The word 'adam' is used over 500 times in the Old Testament and it is almost always translated as mankind, men or man. Very unfortunately the Authorised Version of the Bible, brought out in 1611, wrongly used the proper name Adam in Genesis Chapters 1 to 3. The later Revised Version, brought out in 1884, corrected this and instead of 'Adam' uses 'man'. Most modern translations correctly follow the Revised Version in this respect, although a few still retain Adam (probably out of a misguided deference to tradition rather than to truth!). Incidentally, the word 'Eve' means 'living thing' or 'life'.

Thus at least part of the Genesis account contains metaphors and symbolism, the whole account may have resulted from a series of visions, and the word 'adam' in it means 'representative man'. We may therefore conclude, as did Origen and many others, that the author of Genesis intended the account to be a symbolic description of the origin of the universe, including mankind. Quite clearly Genesis was not intended to be a scientific description.

Genesis, and indeed the whole Bible, was intended for people living at the time the books were written, as well as for succeeding generations. A scientific account of the creation would not only have been totally unintelligible to the people of that time, but also largely unintelligible to most people today! The Genesis creation account needs to be defended not against evolutionists but against the creationists who treat it as a scientific description, which was never intended by the author.

6.4 What does Genesis teach us today?

If the first question to ask in reading the Bible is 'What did the author mean when he wrote this?', the second is 'What does the passage mean to us today? Our interpretation of the Bible must be consistent with our scientific knowledge, because it is the same God who reveals himself to us through the Bible and through creation. Science shows us, beyond reasonable doubt, that life on earth is millions of years old and that one form of life evolved from another, although we do not yet know the detailed mechanisms of evolution. In today's world, Genesis teaches us the following:

a God is the Creator

'In the beginning God created the heavens and the earth' (Gen 1:1). This is the first and most important point of Genesis. God created the universe and all that is in it. Science tells us that the process took millions of years, and also that evolution was the mechanism God used. We should not think of God as someone who created the universe and then went away, like an absentee landlord. In many places in the Bible we read that God not only originally created the universe, but also actively upholds and sustains it all the time. In the words of the Negro spiritual, 'He holds the whole world in his hands'.

b Man is an integral part of nature

'God said "Let the land produce living creatures"' (*Gen 1:24*). 'The Lord God formed man from the dust of the ground' (*Gen 2:7*). Genesis depicts man and other animals as having similar origins: the ground. There is unity throughout all life. In scientific terms, all life is based on DNA.

c Man is the climax of creation

The creation of man occurs last of all, 'on the sixth day'. In scientific terms, man is one of the most recent products of evolution. In terms of intelligence, man is at the top of the evolutionary tree.

d Man is different from the rest of nature

'God created man in his own image' (*Gen 1:26*). As God is a spiritual being, so too does man have a spiritual nature. We alone have the capacity to respond to God. This is true of no other animal.

e Man does wrong

Genesis shows that Adam, representative man, disobeyed God, and both the Old and New Testaments teach that this is true of every man. Some people believe that as man evolves he will get morally better. This is not the teaching of the Bible. History appears to indicate that 20th Century man is morally no better than 1st Century man.

f God loves man

God provided 'trees that were pleasing to the eye and good for food' (*Gen 2:9*). Even after man had disobeyed God, 'The Lord God made garments of skin for the man and his wife and clothed them' (*Gen 3:21*). This love revealed in Genesis foreshadowed God's supreme act of love in sending His son, Jesus, to live and die for mankind.

g Man can choose whether or not to obey God

God said 'Have you eaten from the tree that I commanded you not to eat from?' The man said 'I ate it.' (*Gen 3: 11, 12*). God created us, not like robots, but with freedom. Today, we are free to choose whether or not to obey God, accept his love for us and believe in Jesus Christ.

6.5 The uniqueness of man

In Question 5 at the end of Chapter 4, you had to list characteristics that made humans unique. Try comparing your list with that given three thousand years ago in Genesis, held by many to be a 'primitive account'. The author of Genesis describes man as having the following characteristics:

i *Speech*. The man named the animals (*Gen 2:20*)and he spoke with God (*Gen 3:10*). Speech is a unique characteristic of man.

ii *Moral knowledge* (of good and evil). Man knew good and evil (*Gen 3:3*). Man has far greater moral awareness than any other animal.

iii *Clothing*. Man and woman wore skins for clothing (*Gen 3:21*).

iv *Pain in childbearing* (*Gen 3:16*). This is a fascinating observation. It seems that childbirth is really painful in only one of the millions of species of life on Earth: human beings. The reason for this is the relatively recent development in size of the human brain, which occurred after the evolution of the female pelvis. Thus a human baby's head is now too big to pass comfortably through its mother's pelvis, and childbirth is a painful process. Any further evolution of the female pelvic girdle to increase its size significantly, and hence lead to painfree birth, would lead to difficulty in walking and therefore has not occurred.

v *Agriculture*. Man is capable of working the ground (*Gen 3:23*) to produce food. Animals are not.

vi *Awareness of death (Gen 3:19)*. All plants and animals die. Only man has burial ceremonies. Indeed some scientists date Modern Man from when he started to bury the dead (about 40 000 years ago).

6.6 The Plan and Purpose of Creation

The eminent biologist Jacques Monod stated that 'pure chance, absolutely free but blind, is at the very root of evolution. . . . Neither the duty nor the destiny of man have been written down'. Many non-Christian biologists agree with this.

Christians cannot agree because they believe that life has a plan and purpose. Although some aspects of evolution may appear to be the result of chance, most Christians believe that God is at the very root of evolution. God is in charge. He has a plan and a purpose, and evolution is the way he chose to carry out his creation. If life emerged from a primeval soup then God was the Master Chef.

The photograph at the front of this book shows an electron micrograph of an ant holding a silicon chip. Ask any scientist if the silicon chip was designed and he will say 'of course'. Ask the same scientist if the ant was designed and there is a good chance he will say 'of course not, it evolved'. Yet the ant is far more complex than the silicon chip! Many Christians who are scientists would agree that the ant evolved, but they would also claim that it was designed by the Master Designer. I think this makes sense. Do you? The next chapter will help you decide.

Questions for Discussion

6.1   What are the two basic questions to ask, in understanding the Bible?

6.2   Read the first three chapters of Genesis. Do you think the writer of Genesis intended his creation account to be interpreted literally or not? Give reasons for your answer.

6.3   'The Bible tells us how to go to heaven, not how the heavens go.' What is meant by this quotation? Do you agree with it? Explain why.

6.4   Man is part of nature, but also different from the rest of nature. Explain why.

6.5   Give reasons for whether or not you believe that our existence on earth was planned by God.

7   Summary

At the end of a trial the judge summarises the evidence, suggests some conclusions and then leaves it to the jury to decide. I am going to put on my judge's wig and list the evidence presented in this book, plus the conclusions I think we can draw. The really important decision is then up to you!

The Theories

1   **Evolution** is the theory that all animals and plants have developed from one, or a few, original single cells. Various mechanisms for the process have been proposed. The best-known of these is **Darwinism**: Darwin suggested that evolution occurred slowly and gradually by natural selection in which only the best adapted individuals survived. The process of evolution requires the Earth to be many millions of years old.

2   **Creation** is the belief and God created the universe and all of life. Many Christians believe that evolution is the way in which God chose to create all animals and plants, and they see no conflict between their belief in God as Creator and the scientific theory of evolution.

3   Some Christians believe in **creationism** (also called special creation or creation science). Creationists believe in a literal interpretation of Genesis Chapters 1–3; hence they believe that God directly created the Earth, and all the different animals and plants in it, over a period of six days. Most creationists believe the earth to be between 6000 and 10 000 years old. These ideas completely oppose the theory of evolution and have led to considerable conflict between creationists and evolutionists.

The Evidence

Exhibit A: The Age of the Earth

4   Tree ring dating methods are very reliable and go back over 8000 years. This means that the world cannot have been created 6000 years ago (in 4004 BC), as claimed by some creationists.

5   Radioactive dating methods indicate that the different plants and animals emerged over millions of years, and that the earth itself was formed about 4600 million years ago. This evidence strongly suggests that the belief of creationists in a 'young earth' is wrong.

6   Some creationists explain away the scientific evidence for a very old earth by the **theory of apparent age**. This proposes that the earth was created less than 10 000 years ago, but with an apparent age of millions of years. Christians who believe in evolution argue that the radioactive evidence is God's data to us showing that the Earth really is millions of years old.

Exhibit B: Fossils

7   The fossil record shows that more complex forms of life have successively emerged over many millions of years, measured by radioactive dating methods. Fossils are often contained in rock strata with the earliest forms of life at the bottom and most recent forms at the top. Creationists counter this evidence by proposing that about 5000 years ago there was a world-wide flood, which swept up animals and plants and then deposited them in layers of mud that hardened into rocks. There is no scientific evidence for such a flood, nor for such rapid rock formation.

8   In the fossil record, there is much evidence for evolution on a small scale. However there are also large gaps in the record. In particular there are very few examples of fossils intermediate between major classes of animals.

9   There are three possible explanations of the gaps in the fossil record:
     a direct creation of the major types of plants and animals,
     b evolution occurring mainly in very small, isolated communities,
     c fast evolutionary changes followed by millions of years in which a
        species changed very little.
     Since there are *some* examples of fossils intermediate between major classes of animals we can rule out explanation (a). There is evidence in favour of both (b) and (c). The key question is: How fast have species changed? We do not yet know whether some changes have been so rapid that Darwinism cannot account for them, so that a new evolutionary mechanism is required.

Exhibit C: Genes and Brains

10   All plants and animals are based on the same sort of chemical molecule: DNA. The active length of DNA increases as the organism becomes more complex, for example in going from bacteria to algae to amphibians to reptiles to mammals. This sequence is identical to the sequence showing the dates of appearance of these organisms in the fossil record. This strongly suggests that all life evolved, possibly from a single origin, through the increasing complexity of DNA.

11　The brain of animals also shows a development which is consistent with the date of appearance of the animals in the fossil record. This evidence again strongly favours evolution. There is a particularly good fossil record for the development of the brain of man.

12　Many biologists believe that man is unique because of his brain. The complexity and power of the human brain is far greater than that of any other animal, and gives rise to the ability to read and write books like this one, for example. Although man evolved from other animals, there is now an enormous gap between man and any other living animal.

Exhibit D: The Book of Genesis

13　The correct interpretation of the Genesis creation account has been controversial for many centuries. There are a number of clues which suggest that the writer intended the account to be symbolical and not literally true.

14　The main teaching of Genesis is that God created all of life. Science tells us that this took millions of years and that evolution is the means by which it took place. There is no conflict between the two ideas.

15　Genesis also teaches that man is an integral part of nature, the climax of creation, and unique. This is all consistent with the theory of evolution.

16　Genesis teaches us some things that we cannot learn from the scientific way of looking at the universe. For example, that there is a Creator and that He has a plan and a purpose in his creation. Genesis also teaches that man does wrong, that God loves us and that each of us is able to respond to God.

Summing Up

There are a number of arguments which very strongly suggest that creationism is wrong. That is why most scientists who are Christians reject creationism and instead believe in *both* evolution and creation. They believe that God chose to create everything by a process of evolution. There is a continuous evolutionary trail from the Big Bang to our galaxy, to the Earth, to single-celled animals, to fishes, to reptiles, to mammals and to man. In a sense, God's plan and purpose for mankind were encapsulated in the original Big Bang. He was active in the whole evolutionary process and continues to sustain the world now. What brilliant creative genius to produce the Universe, and life in all its complexity, diversity and beauty, by evolution from a single small beginning.

Some of you who read this book will disagree with the way I have presented the evidence. And some of you will want to find out more. It is important that you reach your own conclusions. To help you make up your minds about evolution, creation and creationism, and to dig deeper, a list of suggestions for further reading is attached.

Further Reading

There is an enormous amount of literature on evolution and creationism. However very few books give a balanced treatment of both. The following books cover a wide spectrum of beliefs, ranging from extreme creationist to out-and-out evolutionist. Each book listed is a good one of its type.

E. H. Andrews, *From Nothing to Nature* (Evangelical Press, 1978). A thoughtful, readable book from a creationist viewpoint, covering quite a wide range of topics.

David Attenborough, *Life on Earth* (Fontana, 1981). A very readable book, arising from a thirteen-part television series. It assumes throughout that evolution is a fact. The colour photographs in the book are stunning.

R. J. Berry, *Adam and the Ape* (Falcon, 1975). A short, well-written book. The author sets out to show that Christianity and evolution are fully compatible.

Jeremy Cherfas (editor), *Darwin Up To Date* (New Science Publications, IPC Ltd, 1983). A series of articles, which originated in the *New Scientist* magazine, on various aspects of evolution.

Charles Darwin, *The Origin of Species* (Murray, 1859). The classic book! Various modern editions are available.

Loren Eiseley, *The Immense Journey* (Vintage, 1957). A beautifully written book, in the style of a novel, about the development of man.

Niles Eldredge, *The Monkey Business* (Washington Square Press, 1982). This book examines the current evolution/creationism controversy in America. It is written by one of the leading proponents of the punctuated equilibrium theory of evolution (the other main proponent being Stephen Jay Gould).

Duane T. Gish, *Evolution: The Fossils Say No!* (Creation-Life, 1972). A book about fossils written by one of America's best-known creationists.

John Gribbin, *Genesis* (Oxford University Press, 1982). About half of the book deals with the origin of the earth and the universe. The other half considers the origin of life and of man. A very readable book, written from an evolutionary standpoint, in which the future of man, as well as his past, is considered.

Francis Hitchin, *The Neck of the Giraffe* (Pan, 1982). A book on creation and evolution written 'from the standpoint of a neutralist passing through the battlefield, attempting to discern where victory will lie' (the words of the author).

Stanley L. Jaki, *Angels, Apes and Men* (Sherwood Sugden, 1982). A more advanced book dealing particularly with philosophical and theological aspects of evolution. Beautifully written.

Philip Kitcher, *Abusing Science: the Case against Creationism* (Open University Press, 1983). A well-informed and clearly-argued book.

Donald M. MacKay, *Brains, Machines and Persons* (Collins, 1980). A book for those who wish to dig deeper into brain mechanisms and human nature.

Jonathan Miller and Borin Van Loon, *Darwin for Beginners* (Writers and Readers Publishing Cooperative, 1982). The cosmic-strip type illustrations occupy well over half of this book on how Darwin's theory developed. The text is by television personality Dr. Jonathan Miller.

H. M. Morris and J. C. Whitcomb, *The Genesis Flood* (Presbyterian and Reformed Publishing Company, 1961; UK edition, Evangelical Press, 1969). Possibly the best-known creationist book. The authors maintain that the earth is less than 10 000 years old and that all the fossils result from the Genesis flood.

Erwin Nemesszeghy and John Russell, *Theology of Evolution* (Mercier Press, 1971). This short book considers some of the theological questions raised by evolution.

Colin Renfrew, *Before Civilisation* (Pelican, 1973). A detailed account of dating methods and their application to prehistoric remains. Written with great clarity.

Carl Sagan, *The Dragons of Eden* (Ballantine, 1977). A fascinating and very readable book on past and future evolution, which was on the *New York Times* bestseller list for 33 weeks.

A. J. Monty White, *What About Origins?* (Dunestone Printers, 1978). A clearly written book presenting the case for creationism.

Donald J. Wiseman, *Clues to Creation in Genesis* (Marshall, Morgan and Scott, 1977). A detailed argument that the 'six days' in the Genesis creation account refer to six days of visions in which the creation story was revealed.